BEST IN CLASS

Dear Student,

Welcome to **BEST IN CLASS, BOOK 2!**

With the skills you are mastering on your instrument, I am sure you are beginning to see how music can add new dimensions to your life.

As you continue to study, you will quickly see that with more proficiency on your instrument comes a greater experience of the beauty and joy of music.

To play your instrument well, careful practice is essential. You will find a chart below to help you keep track of your practice time. Always strive to do your best.

Best wishes in reaching your musical goals!

Bruce Pearson

PRACTICE RECORD CHART

WEEK	DAY 1	DAY 2	DAY 3	DAY 4	DAY 5	DAY 6	DAY 7	TOTAL TIME	PARENT'S INITIALS	WEEKLY GRADE
1										
2										
3										
4										
5										
6										
7										
8										
9										
10										
11										
12										
13										
14										
15										
16										
17										
18										

WEEK	DAY 1	DAY 2	DAY 3	DAY 4	DAY 5	DAY 6	DAY 7	TOTAL TIME	PARENT'S INITIALS	WEEKLY GRADE
19										
20										
21										
22										
23										
24										
25										
26										
27										
28										
29										
30										
31										
32										
33										
34										
35										
36										

© 1983 Kjos West, Publisher, San Diego, California
BN 0-8497-5881-5   All Rights Reserved   International Copyright Secured   Printed in U.S.A.   W4TP

DAILY WARM-UPS . . . for cornets/trumpets only

A. STEADY TONE

★ Always play with your best tone. Keep your tone steady.
1. Play each note *p* ◁=*f*=▷ *p*
2. Play each note with the following articulation pattern: ♩ ♩ ♫♫. Strive for a clean attack on each note.

B. LIP SLURS

★ Using the same pattern, continue downward with the following fingerings: ●●○ , ○●● , ●○● , ●●●

C. TECHNIC TRAINER

★ Play this exercise again using each of the following articulations: A. ♫♫♫ B. ♫♫♫ C. ♫♫

D. INTERVAL STRETCH

★ Use the appropriate syllables (Toh, Tah, Tee) to play each interval accurately.

1. MOVING CHORDS

Band Arrangement

2. TECHNIC TRAINER

3. C MAJOR (B♭ Concert) SCALE, THIRDS, AND ARPEGGIOS

★ Write in the note names before you play.

THEORY
GAME

NEW IDEA

| ACCENT | | Play the note with the accent (>) a little louder. |

11. LITTLE BROWN JUG

Joe Winner

NEW IDEA

| EIGHTH REST | 𝄾 = 1/2 beat of silence

An eighth rest is half as long as a quarter rest. | 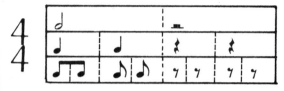 |

THEORY GAMES

1. Before you play exercises 12 through 16, write in the counting. 2. Then clap and count the rhythm.

12. REST ON THREE

13. REST ON TWO

14. REST ON FOUR

15. REST OFF THE BEAT

16. REST ON THE BEAT

17. THE GOOD KING HAS RHYTHM

SOMETHING SPECIAL . . . for cornets/trumpets only

SPECIAL EXERCISE

W4TP

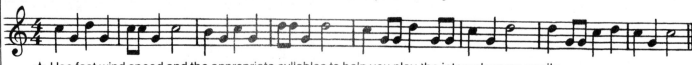

★ Use fast wind speed and the appropriate syllables to help you play the intervals more easily.

NEW IDEA

SYNCOPATION		Play an accent on a note that is normally not a strong pulse.

18. PLAY IT STRONG

★ Write in the counting before you play.

19. SHOO-FLY

Frank Campbell

20. NOBODY KNOWS THE TROUBLE I'VE SEEN

Spiritual

21. LIZA JANE

Afro-American Folk Song

22. A LATIN LUNCH

Root/Pearson — Band Arrangement

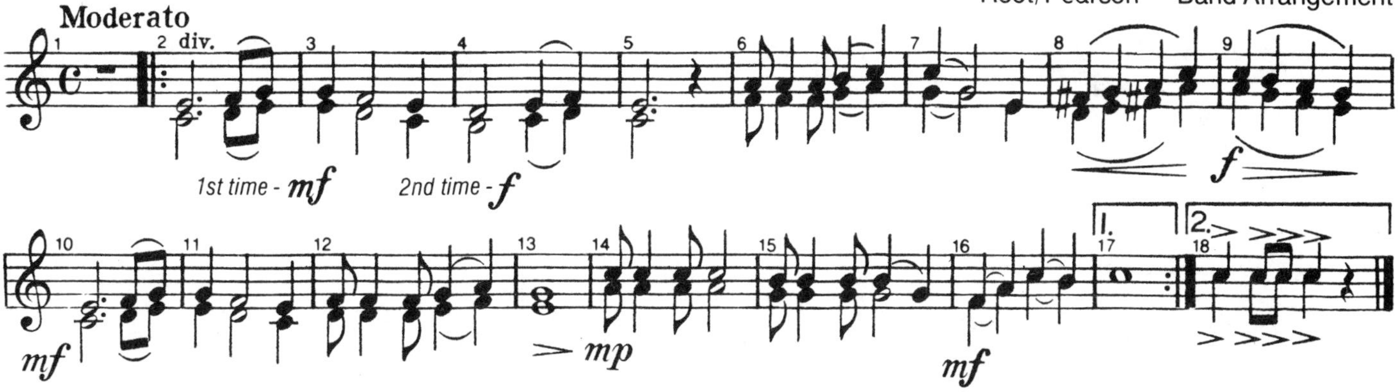

NEW IDEA

LONG REST	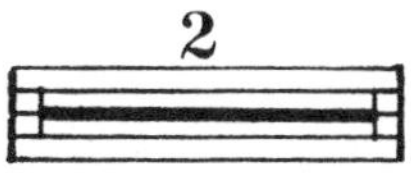	Rest for the number of measures that are indicated.

23. HOW LONG IS YOUR REST?

Count: 1,2 — 2,2

SPECIAL EXERCISE

NEW NOTES

SOMETHING SPECIAL . . . for cornets/trumpets only

1st time - play the lower notes *2nd time - play the upper notes*

★ These two notes are enharmonic.

6

NEW IDEA

ONE MEASURE REPEAT		Repeat the previous measure.

24. THE TENDERFOOT POLKA

Allegro

Root/Pearson — Band Arrangement

★ Write in the counting before you play.

NEW IDEA

KEY SIGNATURE	 Key Name: B♭ Major (A♭ Concert)	When you see this key signature, play all B's as B flats and all E's as E flats.

NEW NOTE / THEORY GAME

25. B♭ MAJOR (A♭ Concert) SCALE AND ARPEGGIOS

★ Circle the notes changed by the key signature before you play.

26. SIMILAR SOUNDS

★ These two notes are enharmonic.

NEW NOTES

27. OLD JOE CLARK

Moderato

Tennessee Folk Song

NEW NOTES

28. CHROMATIC CAPERS

29. ENHARMONIC HOP

Moderato

W4TP

SOMETHING SPECIAL . . . for cornets/trumpets only

SPECIAL XERCISES

NEW IDEAS

THEORY GAME

C MAJOR KEY NAME	(music staff)	If there are no flats or sharps in the key signature, the key name is C Major.
FLAT KEY NAMES (Major Keys)		1. Look at the next-to-the-last flat from the right in the key signature. 2. The letter name of that flat is the name of the Major key. EXAMPLE: Key of E♭ Major  3. If there is one flat in the key signature, the key name is F Major.

A. KEY NAME GAME

★ Write in the key name for each key signature.

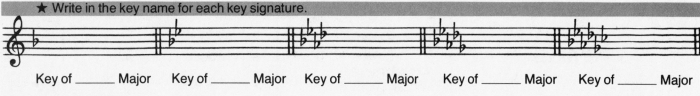

Key of _____ Major   Key of _____ Major   Key of _____ Major   Key of _____ Major   Key of _____ Major

B. LIP SLURS

Tah, oh, ah, ee,   ah, oh, ah, ee, ah

1. Using the same pattern, continue downward with the following fingerings: ●●○ , ○●● , ●○● , ●●●
2. Play this exercise again on your mouthpiece only.

C. E♭ MAJOR (D♭ Concert) SCALE, THIRDS, AND ARPEGGIOS

D. ARTICULATION ETUDE

★ Play this exercise again using each of the following articulations:

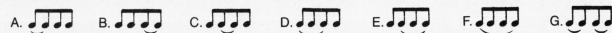

A.   B.   C.   D.   E.   F.   G.

E. LEGATO ETUDE

p —— f $>$ p —— f p $<$ f $>$ p

F. BUGLE CALL

W4TP

THEORY
GAME

THEORY
GAME

NEW IDEA

30. KEY SIGNATURE CRAZE
★ Circle the notes changed by each key signature before you play.

31. SONATINA
Ludwig van Beethoven
★ What is the key name for **SONATINA**? _____

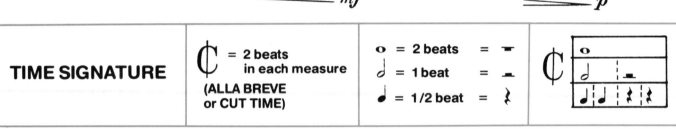

TIME SIGNATURE	𝄵 = 2 beats in each measure (ALLA BREVE or CUT TIME)	o = 2 beats = 𝄼 ; ♩ = 1 beat = ; ♪ = 1/2 beat = 𝄾	𝄵

32. CUT TIME

★ Write in the counting before you play.

33. OATS AND BEANS
American Folk Song

34. OH, SUSANNA
Stephen Foster

★ Write in the counting before you play.

35. STARS AND STRIPES FOREVER
John Philip Sousa

SPECIAL
EXERCISE

NEW NOTE

SOMETHING SPECIAL . . . for cornets/trumpets only

W4TP

THEORY GAME

36. MARK TIME MARCH

Root/Pearson — Band Arrangement

★ What is the key name for **MARK TIME MARCH?** _____

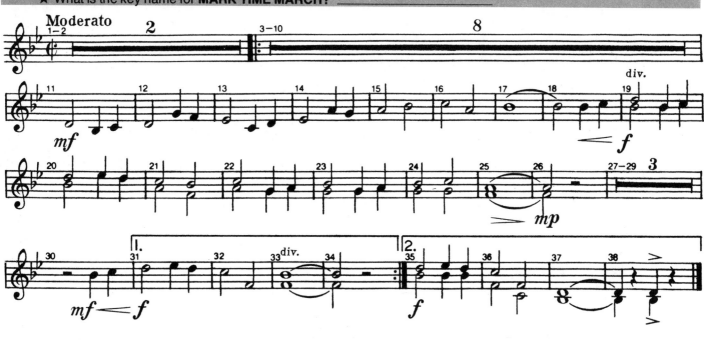

NEW IDEAS

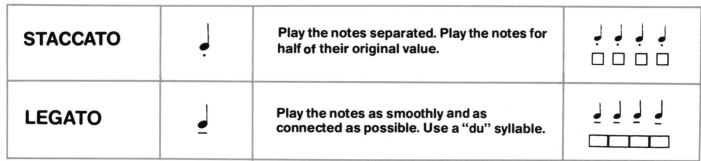

37. STACCATO AND LEGATO

★ Separate the staccato notes and sustain the legato notes.

38. THEME FROM "SURPRISE SYMPHONY"

Franz Joseph Haydn

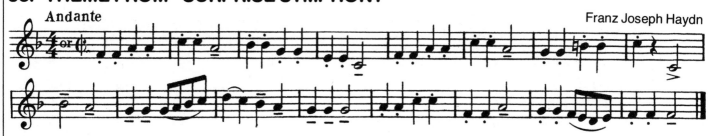

NEW IDEA

SIMILE	*simile* (*sim.*)	Continue in the same way.

39. TECHNIC TRAINER

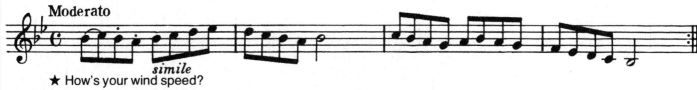

★ How's your wind speed?

SPECIAL EXERCISE

SOMETHING SPECIAL . . . for cornets/trumpets only

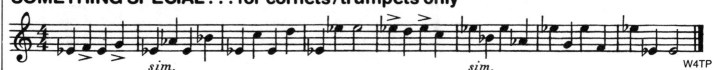

W4TP

D.S. AL FINE	$D.\,S.\,(del\;segno)=$ **sign** $Fine$ = **finish**	When you see the $D.\,S.\,al\;Fine$, **go back to the** 𝄋 **(sign) and stop when you come to the** $Fine$.

40. THE ASH GROVE

Old Welsh Air

THEORY GAME

41. CRIPPLE CREEK

Traditional

★ Write in the note names before you play.

42. TECHNIC TRAINER

★Constant air and quick fingers will make this easier!

NEW NOTE

43. LITTLE DANCE

Franz Joseph Haydn

★ Write in the counting before you play.

SPECIAL EXERCISE

NEW NOTES

SOMETHING SPECIAL . . . for cornets/trumpets only

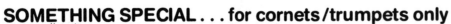

★ These two notes are enharmonic.

44. THE HIGH SCHOOL CADETS MARCH

John Philip Sousa

45. MARACAS GO UP AND DOWN

Mexican Folk Song

SIXTEEN NOTE — A sixteenth note is half as long as an eighth note. = 1/4 beat

46. RHYTHM MIX

★ Write in the counting before you play.

47. OLD BRASS WAGON

Southern Tune

48. JING-A-LING

American Camp Song

49. STEADY AS YOU GO

★ What is the key name for **STEADY AS YOU GO?**

50. TECHNIC TRAINER

SOMETHING SPECIAL . . . for cornets/trumpets only

mp < f > simile   f ——— mp

W4TP

NEW IDEA

THEORY GAME

SPECIAL EXERCISE

51. SOURWOOD MOUNTAIN

Moderato

American Folk Song

mf

EIGHTH AND SIXTEENTH NOTE COMBINATIONS

NEW IDEA

52. GRASSHOPPERS' GIG

★ Write in the counting before you play.

53. HOPPER-GRASS HOP

★ Write in the counting before you play.

54. EZEKIEL SAW THE WHEEL

Moderato

Spiritual

mp

mf

mp

KEY SIGNATURE

Key Name: D Major (C Concert)

When you see this key signature, play all F's as F sharps and all C's as C sharps.

NEW IDEA

55. D MAJOR (C Concert) SCALE

★ Circle the notes changed by the key signature before you play.

C#

NEW NOTE

THEORY GAME

56. CHROMATIC SCALE

A# Db

enharmonic

NEW NOTES

SOMETHING SPECIAL . . . for cornets/trumpets only

1. 2. 3. 4. 5. 6.

SPECIAL EXERCISE

W4TP

1. Play each measure 4 times. 2. Practice each measure both tongued and slurred.

SOMETHING SPECIAL . . . for cornets/trumpets only

SPECIAL EXERCISES

NEW IDEA

THEORY GAME

SHARP KEY NAMES (Major Keys)

1. Look at the last sharp to the right in the key signature.
2. The letter name of the next line or space above is the name of the Major key.

EXAMPLE: Key of D Major

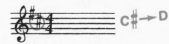

3. If there are six sharps in the key signature, the key name is F♯ Major.

4. If there are seven sharps in the key signature, the key name is C♯ Major.

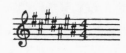

A. KEY NAME GAME

★ Write in the key name for each key signature.

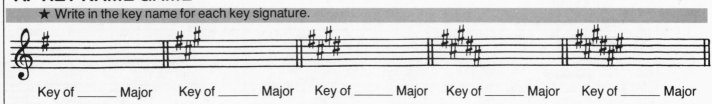

Key of _____ Major   Key of _____ Major   Key of _____ Major   Key of _____ Major   Key of _____ Major

B. LIP SLURS

1. Using the same pattern, continue downward with following fingerings: ●●○, ○●●, ●○●, ●●●
2. Play this exercise again on your mouthpiece only.

C. FANFARE

D. CHROMATIC ETUDE

E. KNUCKLE BUSTERS

★ Play each measure 4 times.

W4TP

14

THEORY
GAME

57. MARIANNI
Italian Folk Song

★ What is the form of **MARIANNI?** _____

NEW NOTE

58. MOVIN' ON UP

59. THE RIDDLE SONG
American Folk Song

THEORY
GAME

60. TECHNIC TRAINER
★ What is the key name for **TECHNIC TRAINER?** _____

61. IRISH JIG
Irish Folk Song

62. MUSETTE
Johann Sebastian Bach

63. CAN YOU GUESS MY NAME?

★ Write in the counting before you play.

SOMETHING SPECIAL . . . for cornets/trumpets only

Toh Tah Tee *simile*

★Tighten your embouchure in toward the center as you go higher.

SPECIAL
EXERCISE

W4TP

64. ARTICULATION ANTICS

Moderato

TIME SIGNATURE	$\frac{6}{8}$ = 6 beats in each measure = ♪ receives 1 beat	♩. = 6 beats = ▬ ♩. = 3 beats = 𝄾. ♩ = 2 beats = 𝄾 ♪ = 1 beat = 𝄾	$\frac{6}{8}$

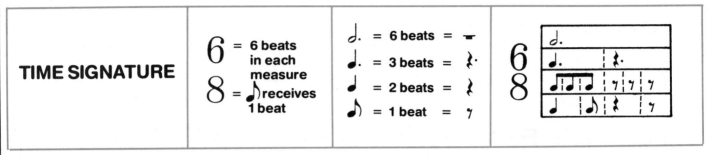

65. COUNT ON IT

1. Count out loud and write in the counting before you play.   2. Clap the rhythm before you play.

66. THE BEAT GOES ON

★Did you feel 6 beats in each ♩. ?

67. THREE IN ONE

★Feel 3 beats in each ♩. .

68. TWO IS BETTER THAN ONE

★ Be sure to give the ♩ 2 beats.

69. OFF AND ON

70. FIDDLE-DEE-DEE

Allegro

English Folk Song

SOMETHING SPECIAL . . . for cornets/trumpets only

W4TP

NEW IDEA

TIME SIGNATURE	$\frac{3}{8}$ = 3 beats in each measure = ♪ receives 1 beat	♩. = 3 beats = 𝄽 ♩ = 2 beats = 𝄽 ♪ = 1 beat = 𝄾	

71. DUET FOR HAND CLAPPERS AND KNEE SLAPPERS
Hand Clappers

Knee Slappers

72. TECHNIC TRAINER

★ Write in the counting and clap the rhythm before you play.

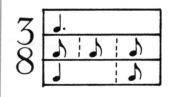

NEW IDEA

D.S. AL CODA	*D. S. (del segno)* = sign *al Coda* = to Coda	When you see the *D. S. al Coda* go back to the 𝄋 (sign). When you come to the ⊕ (Coda sign), skip to the Coda.

73. BACK TO THE 50'S

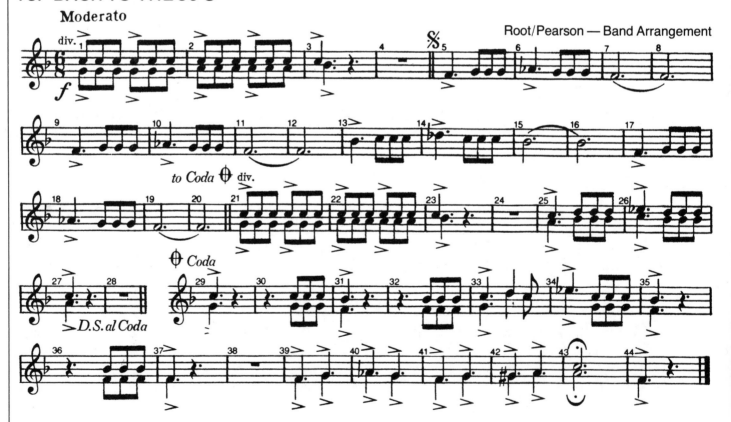

Moderato

Root/Pearson — Band Arrangement

SOMETHING SPECIAL . . . for cornets/trumpets only

SPECIAL EXERCISE
 W4TP

74. TECHNIC TRAINER

75. EIGHTH NOTES AND RESTS

76. GERMAN DANCE

Franz Joseph Haydn

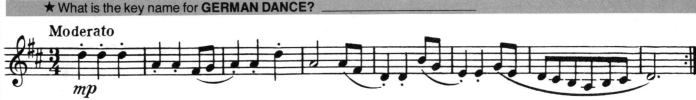

★ What is the key name for **GERMAN DANCE?** _____

THEORY
GAME

77. VIVE LA COMPAGNIE

French Folk Song

SOMETHING SPECIAL . . . for cornets/trumpets only

SPECIAL
EXERCISE

W4TP

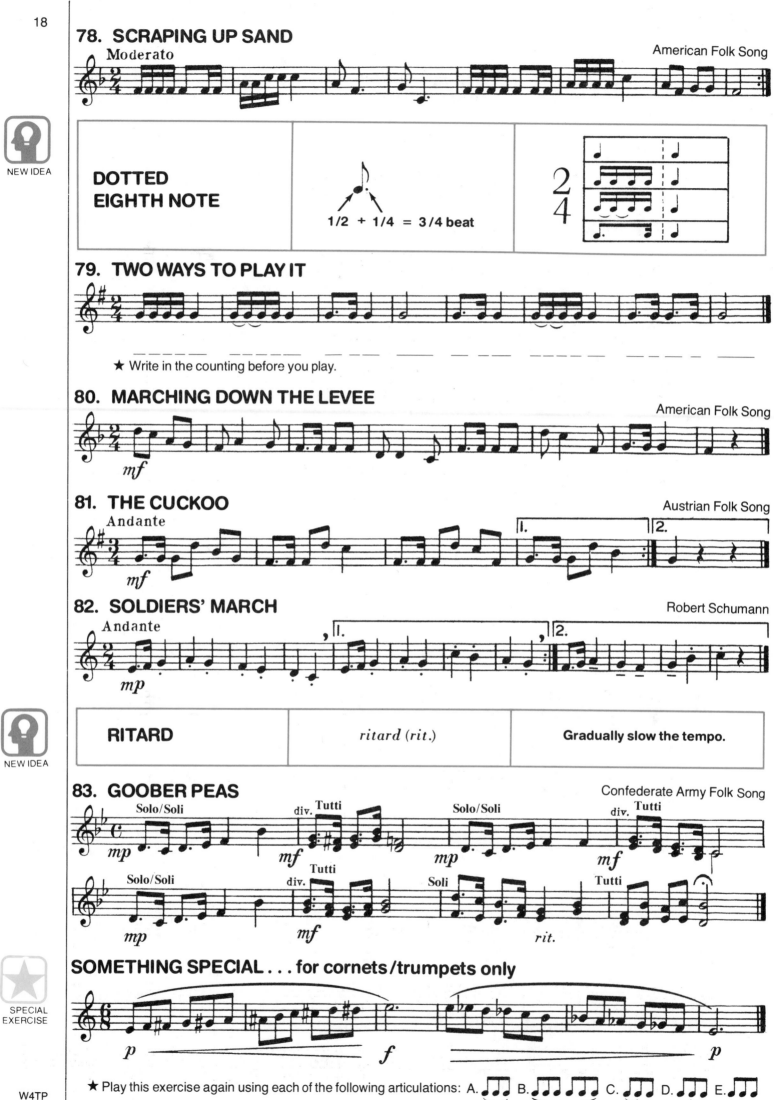

78. SCRAPING UP SAND

Moderato

American Folk Song

DOTTED EIGHTH NOTE	1/2 + 1/4 = 3/4 beat	$\frac{2}{4}$

79. TWO WAYS TO PLAY IT

★ Write in the counting before you play.

80. MARCHING DOWN THE LEVEE

American Folk Song

mf

81. THE CUCKOO

Austrian Folk Song

Andante

mf

82. SOLDIERS' MARCH

Robert Schumann

Andante

mp

RITARD	*ritard (rit.)*	**Gradually slow the tempo.**

83. GOOBER PEAS

Confederate Army Folk Song

Solo/Soli   div. Tutti   Solo/Soli   div. Tutti

mp   *mf*   *mp*   *mf*

Solo/Soli   div. Tutti   Soli   Tutti

mp   *mf*   *rit.*

SOMETHING SPECIAL . . . for cornets/trumpets only

p   *f*   *p*

★ Play this exercise again using each of the following articulations: A. B. C. D. E.

NEW IDEA

NEW IDEA

SPECIAL EXERCISE

W4TP

| DYNAMICS | $\textbf{\textit{ff}}$ = *fortissimo* | Play with a very loud volume. |
| | $\textbf{\textit{pp}}$ = *pianissimo* | Play with a very soft volume. |

MAGIC MOUNTAIN

Root/Pearson

W4TP

84. THE HUNTING HORN

4-Part Round

85. TECHNIC TRAINER

★ What is the key name for **TECHNIC TRAINER?** _____

86. BEST IN CLASS POLKA

Root/Pearson — Band Arrangement

87. AMERICAN PATROL

Frank W. Meacham

★ Write in the counting before you play.

SOMETHING SPECIAL . . . for cornets/trumpets only

SPECIAL EXERCISE

88. CONTRA-DANSE
Wolfgang Amadeus Mozart

★ What is the form of CONTRA-DANSE?

89. MARCH OF THE KINGS
Georges Bizet

EW NOTE

90. RANGE DEVELOPER

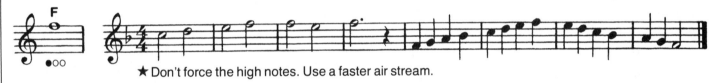

★ Don't force the high notes. Use a faster air stream.

91. TECHNIC TRAINER

92. SKIP TO MY LOU
American Folk Song

★ Tonguing is easier when you use a continuous air stream.

SPECIAL
EXERCISE

SOMETHING SPECIAL . . . for cornets/trumpets only

Toh Tah Tee

★ Practice this exercise to build your range.

W4TP

93. EL CAPITAN MARCH

John Philip Sousa

Allegro

94. CAN YOU COUNT IT?

Moderato

★ Write in the counting before you play.

NEW IDEA

KEY SIGNATURE	 Key Name: E♭ Major (D♭ Concert)	When you see this key signature, play all B's as B flats, all E's as E flats, and all A's as A flats.

THEORY GAME

95. E♭ MAJOR (D♭ Concert) SCALE, THIRDS, AND ARPEGGIOS

★ Circle the notes that are changed by the key signature before you play.

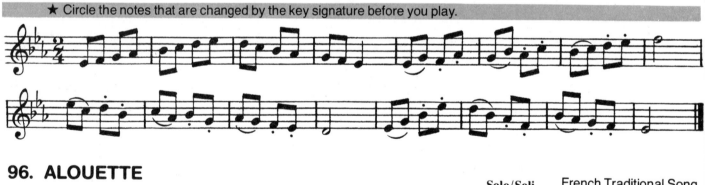

96. ALOUETTE

French Traditional Song

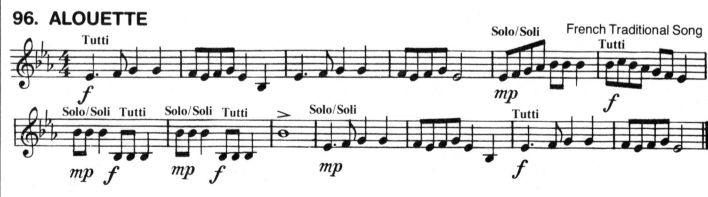

SOMETHING SPECIAL . . . for cornets/trumpets only

SPECIAL EXERCISE

★ Play each measure 4 times.

SOMETHING SPECIAL . . . for cornets/trumpets only

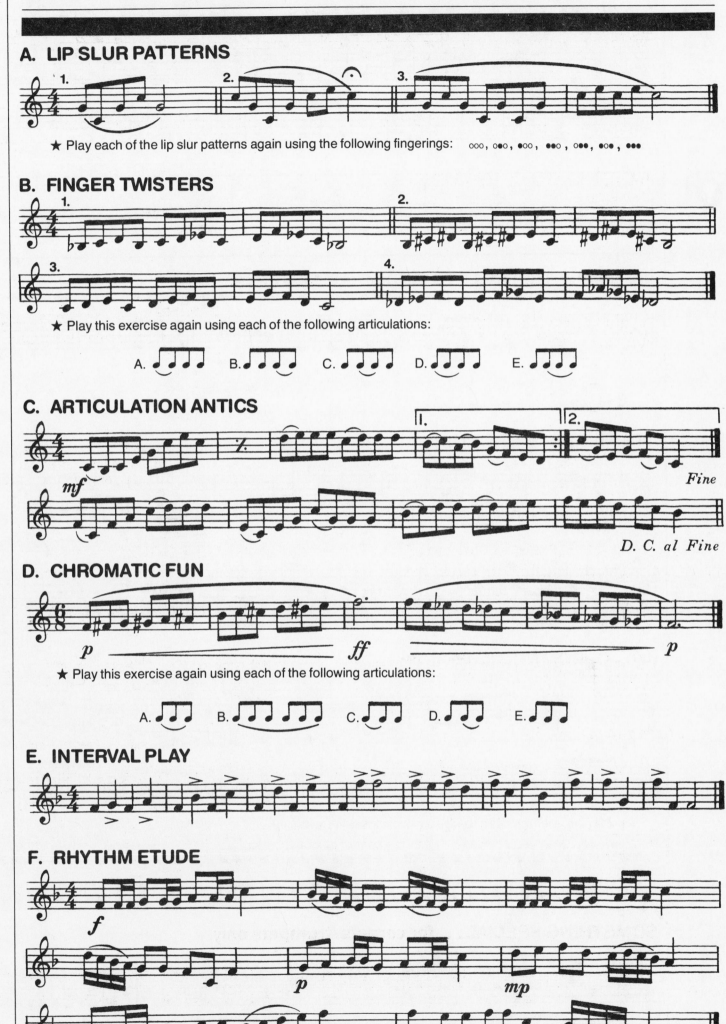

A. LIP SLUR PATTERNS

★ Play each of the lip slur patterns again using the following fingerings: ○○○, ○●○, ●○○, ●●○, ○●●, ●○●, ●●●

B. FINGER TWISTERS

★ Play this exercise again using each of the following articulations:

A.   B.   C.   D.   E.

C. ARTICULATION ANTICS

mf

Fine

D. C. al Fine

D. CHROMATIC FUN

p   *ff*   *p*

★ Play this exercise again using each of the following articulations:

A.   B.   C.   D.   E.

E. INTERVAL PLAY

F. RHYTHM ETUDE

f

p   *mp*

mf   *f*

W4TP

97. DOWN BY THE STATION
2-Part Round

★ What is the key name for **DOWN BY THE STATION?** _____

TRIPLET — Each note receives 1/3 of a beat.

98. TRIPLETS, TRIPLETS, AND MORE TRIPLETS

★ Write in the counting before you play.

99. PILGRIMS' CHORUS
Richard Wagner

100. CHROMATIC CAPERS

★ Play this exercise again using each of the following articulations:

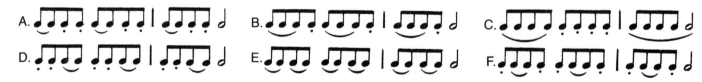

SOMETHING SPECIAL . . . for cornets/trumpets only

★ Using the same pattern, continue downward with the following fingerings: ●○○, ●●○, ○●●, ●○●, ●●●

101. ROLLIN' ROCK

Root/Pearson — Band Arrangement

102. TECHNIC TRAINER

103. OUT FOR THE COUNT

★ Write in the counting before you play.

SOMETHING SPECIAL . . . for cornets/trumpets only

SPECIAL EXERCISE

★ Play each measure 4 times.

W4TP

104. CAN-CAN

Jacques Offenbach

Allegro

105. TONGUING TRAINER

Moderato

★ Write in the counting before you play.

106. MARCH FROM "NUTCRACKER SUITE"

Peter Ilyich Tchaikovsky

Moderato

107. TECHNIC TRAINER

Andante

SOMETHING SPECIAL . . . for cornets/trumpets only

★ Play this exercise again using each of the following articulations:

A.   B.   C.   D.   E.

SPECIAL
EXERCISE

108. CHROMATIC SCALE

★ Memorize this scale.

109. ARKANSAS TRAVELER

Folk Song

Moderato

mf

opt.

opt.

110. FATHER OF VICTORY

L. Ganne

f ★Are you playing with a constant air stream and a good hand position?

111. CAN YOU COUNT IT?

Fine

★ Write in the counting before you play.

D.C. al Fine

SIXTEENTH REST	♪ = 1/4 beat of silence A sixteenth rest is half as long as an eighth rest.	

NEW IDEA

THEORY GAME

112. SIXTEENTH STUDY

1. On each of the following exercises, write in the counting before you play. 2. Play each exercise 4 times.

A.

B.

C.

D.

28

113. THE GLENDY BURK

Stephen Foster

Moderato

★ Write in the counting before you play.

114. RULE BRITANNIA

English Folk Song

Moderato

mf *f* *rit.*

115. THEME FROM "SWAN LAKE"

Peter Ilyich Tchaikovsky

Andante

p

★ Write in a breath mark at the end of each phrase.

Fine

mf *p* *f* *rit.*

D. C. al Fine

116. TECHNIC TRAINER

★ What is the key name for **TECHNIC TRAINER**? _____

THEORY GAME

Allegro

SOMETHING SPECIAL . . . for cornets/trumpets only

SPECIAL EXERCISE

W4TP

SOMETHING SPECIAL . . . for cornets/trumpets only

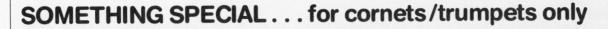

A. RANGE BUILDER

B. FABULOUS FOURTHS

1st time - *f*   2nd time - *p*

C. SYNCOPATED REVIEW

D. ARTICULATION ANTICS

E. FAR OUT FIFTHS

NEW NOTES

F. FLUID FINGERS

W4TP

117. MARCH FROM "AIDA"

Giuseppe Verdi

118. OUR DIRECTOR MARCH

F.E. Bigelow

THEORY
GAME

119. BATTLE HYMN OF THE REPUBLIC

William Steffe

★ What is the key name for **BATTLE HYMN OF THE REPUBLIC?** _____

120. MARCH FOR DEE

Root/Pearson — Band Arrangement

W4TP

SCALE STUDIES